Theres a road with two yellow lines it goes on for years. And the people there smile and wave, its not like back home. In the doorway, where the evening sky lights up my room lights up my room, lights up my room, lights up my.. Times are fierce then times are fine, yeah it goes that way. Down some highway, down some lonely road in an old fashioned way. In the garden, where the evening sky lights up my room, lights up my room, lights up my room, lights up my.. & the darkness lets them see all all of the people they never knew. So float into space, falling through puddles in places I've never been. Will my soul be angry, when you die do you feel alright? In the garden, where the evening sky lights up my room, lights up my room, lights up my room, lights up my.

TURIN BRAKES

the Optimist Lp

guitar tablature vocal

Published 2001

© International Music Publications Ltd
Griffin House 161 Hammersmith Road London W6 8BS England

Production Anna Joyce
Folio Design Dominic Brookman
Music Arranged by Artemis Music Ltd
Cover photography by Christophe Rihet
Interior Artwork by Izabella@lavapepper

Feeling Oblivion

Words and Music by Olly Knights and Gale Paridjanian

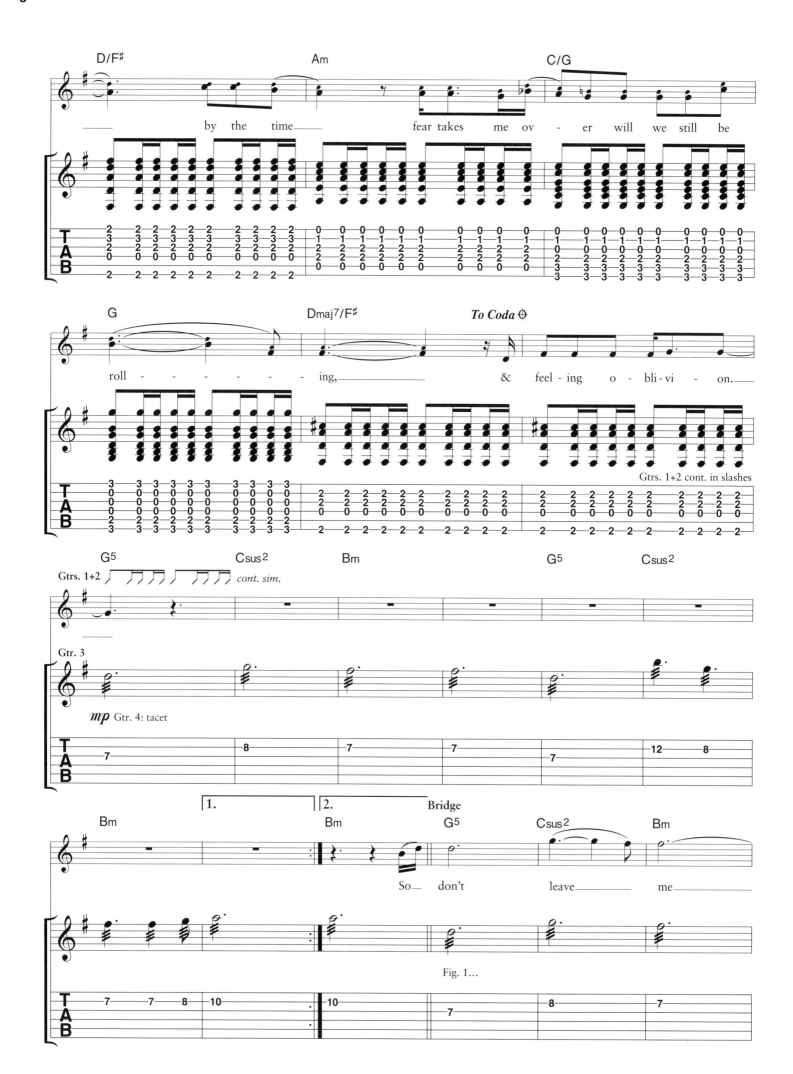

Underdog (Save Me)

Words and Music by Olly Knights and Gale Paridjanian

16

Verse 3:
Well I've been dreaming of jetstreams and kicking up dust,
A thirty seven thousand foot wanderlust and
With skyline number 9 ticked off in my mind,
Oh can you hear me screaming out now through
The telephone line.

Oh please save me *etc.*

Emergency 72

Words and Music by Olly Knights and Gale Paridjanian

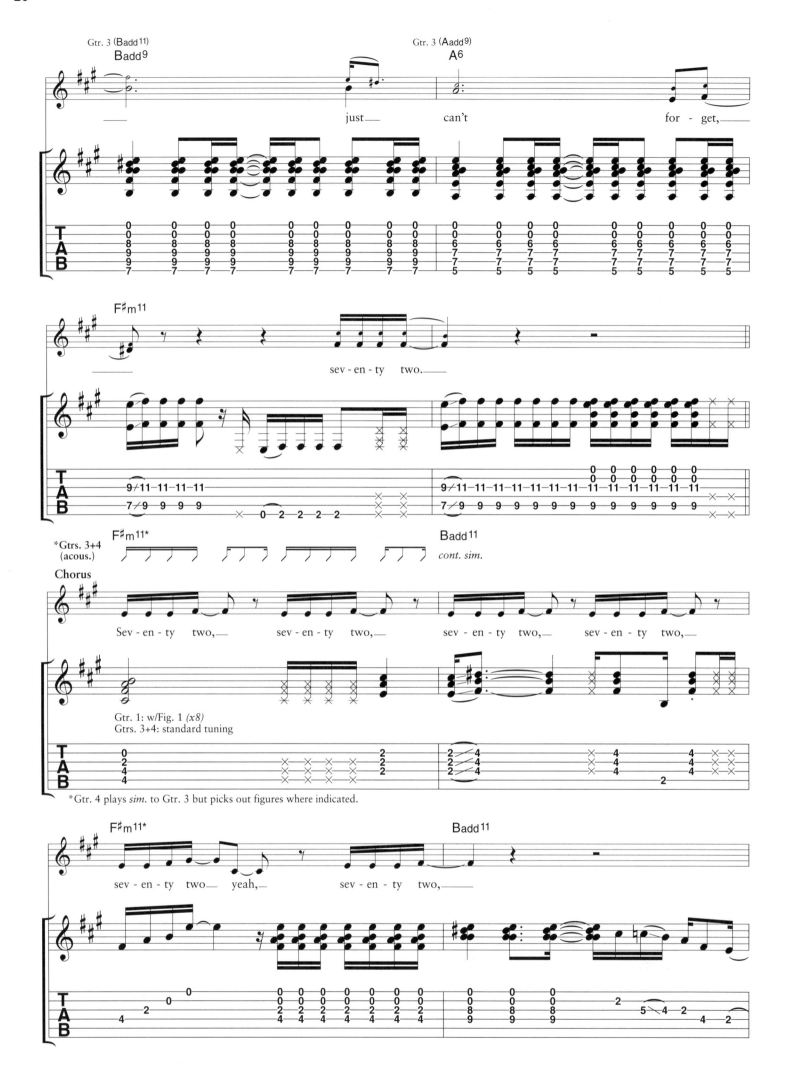

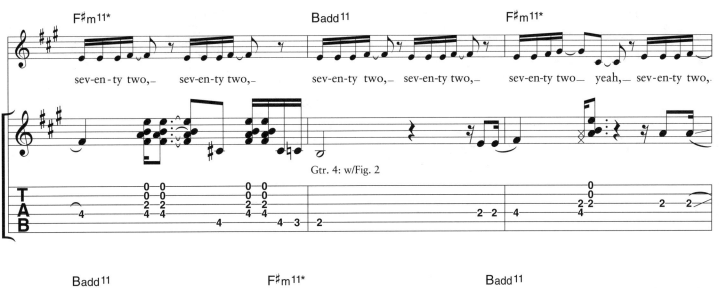

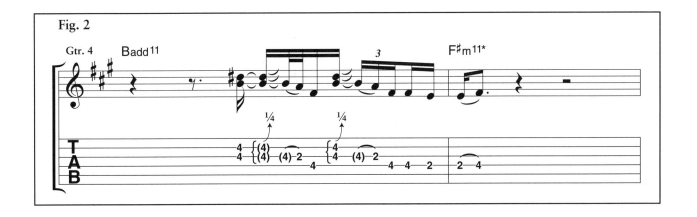

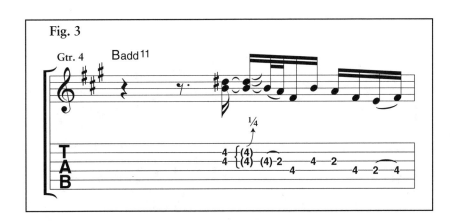

Fig. 4

Future Boy

Words and Music by Olly Knights and Gale Paridjanian

%

Verse

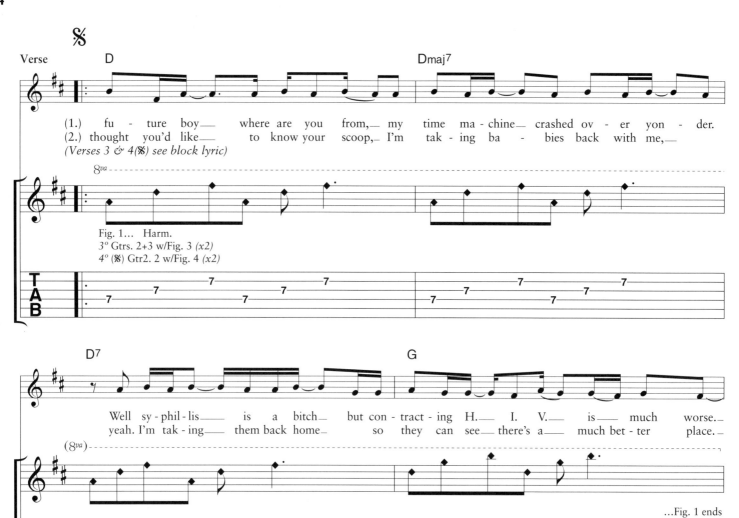

(1.) fu - ture boy___ where are you from,___ my time ma - chine___ crashed ov - er yon - der.
(2.) thought you'd like___ to know your scoop, I'm tak - ing ba - bies back with me,___
(Verses 3 & 4(%)) see block lyric)

8va -

Fig. 1... Harm.
3° Gtrs. 2+3 w/Fig. 3 (x2)
4° (%) Gtr2. 2 w/Fig. 4 (x2)

Well sy - phil - lis___ is a bitch___ but con - tract - ing H. I. V.___ is___ much worse.___
yeah. I'm tak - ing___ them back home___ so they can see___ there's a___ much bet - ter place.___

(8va) -

...Fig. 1 ends

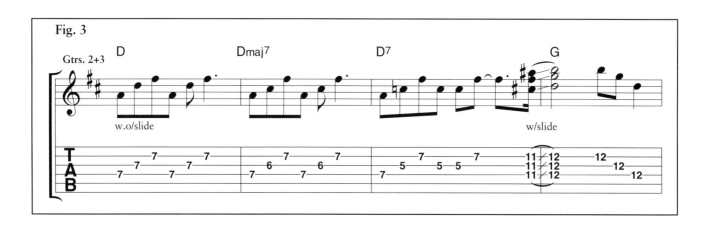

Fig. 3

Gtrs. 2+3

D   Dmaj7   D7   G

w.o/slide   w/slide

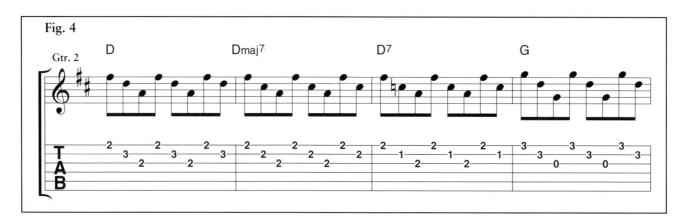

Fig. 4

Gtr. 2

D   Dmaj7   D7   G

Verse 3:
As long as they don't use monkeys,
We enjoy the heat of stolen days
In the summer of '93.
Well the future boy said I've got friends
But you know sometimes it all depends
On how tall they are against yourself.

Verse 4:
My friends have all gone and left me
So I decided to come here and see myself as a baby,
But it looks like I'm stuck here this time, oh shit,
I'm gonna miss my friends.

No you're still the future boy (etc.)

The Door

Words and Music by Olly Knights and Gale Paridjanian

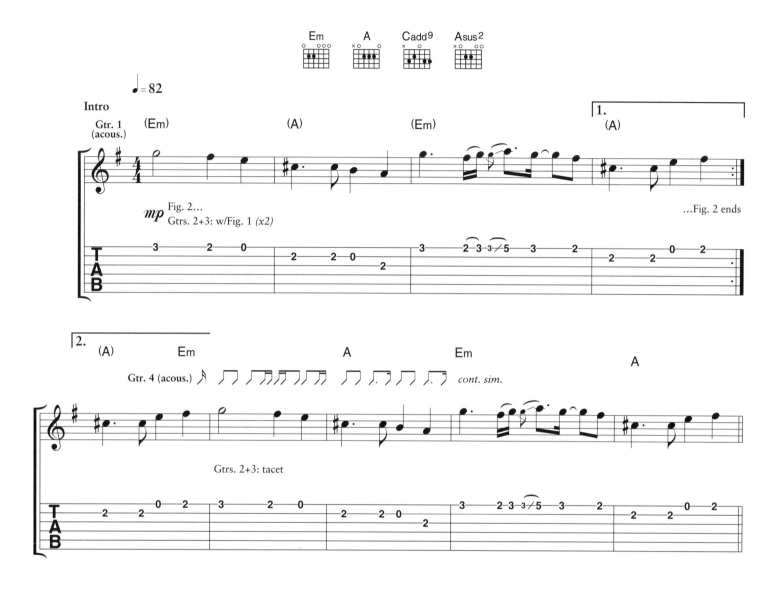

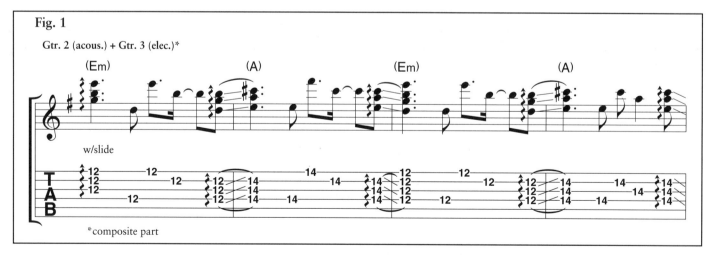

Fig. 1

Gtr. 2 (acous.) + Gtr. 3 (elec.)*

*composite part

30

Chorus %

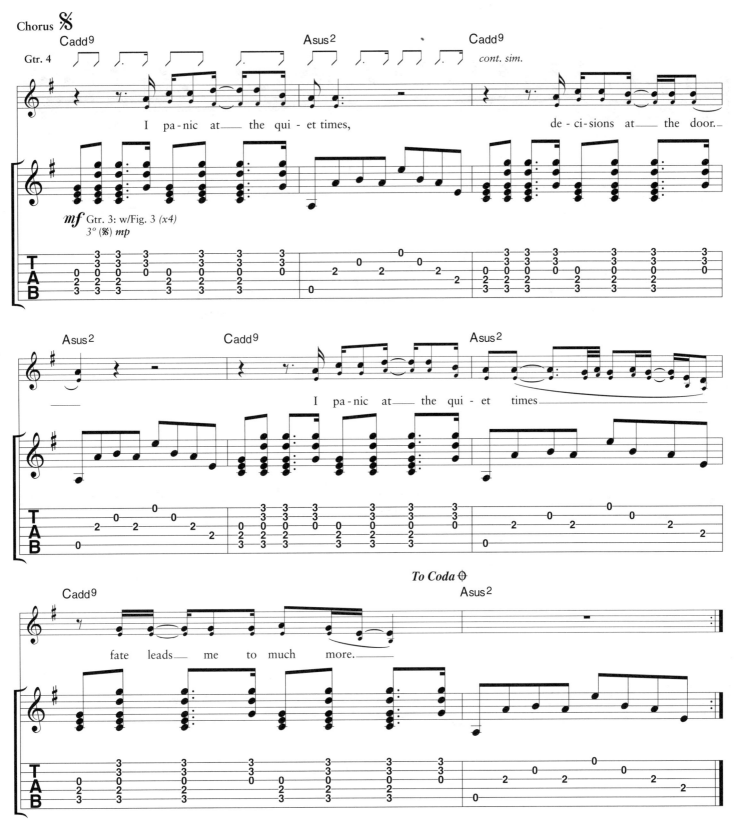

To Coda ⊕

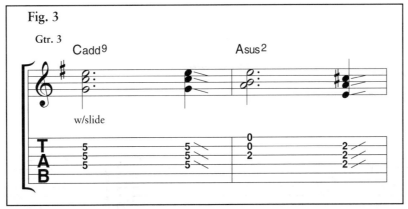

Fig. 3

Gtr. 3

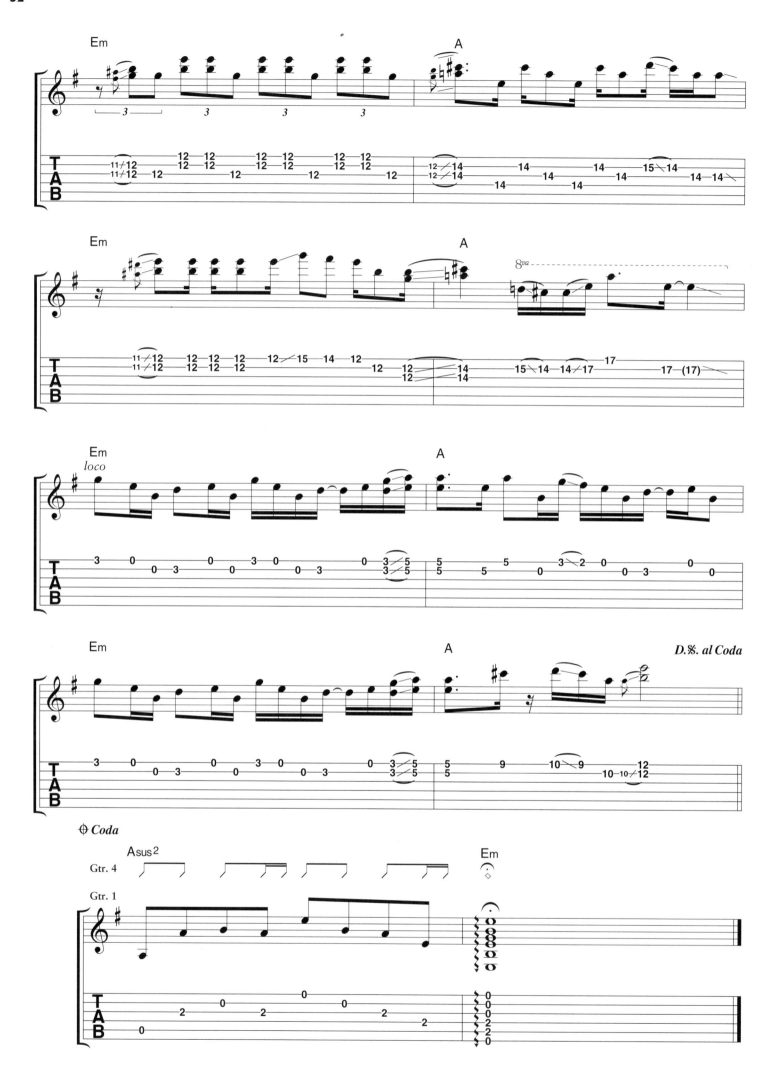

State Of Things

Words and Music by Olly Knights and Gale Paridjanian

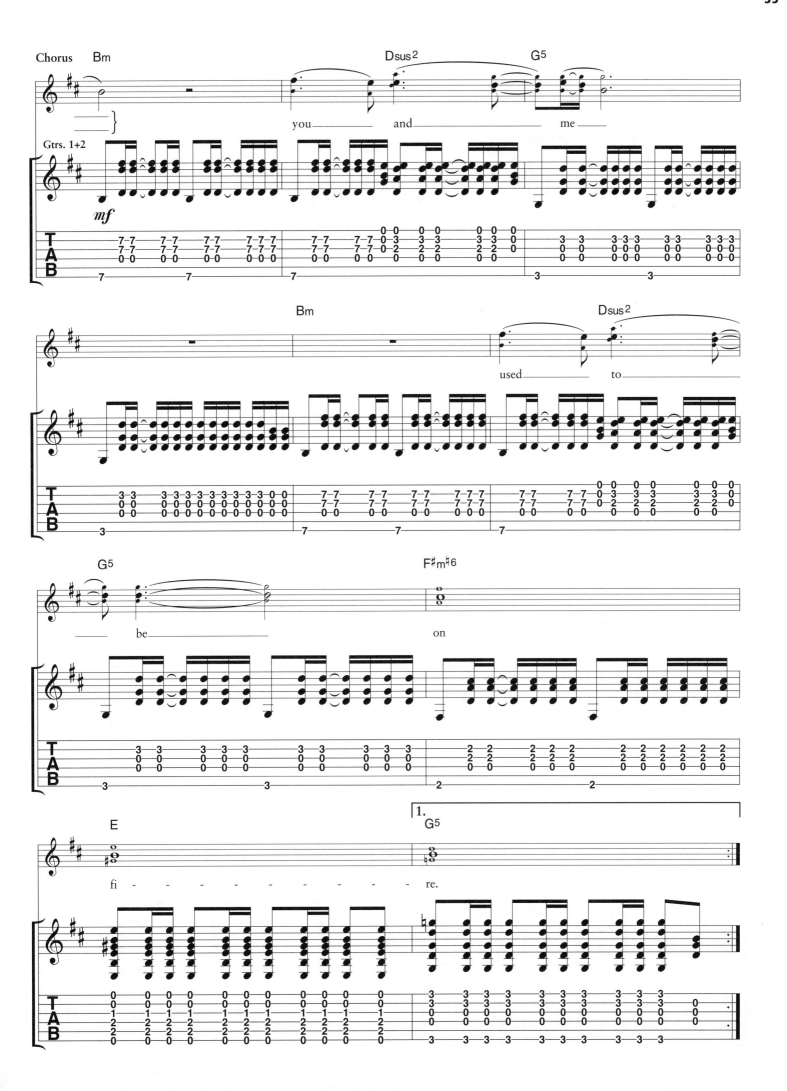

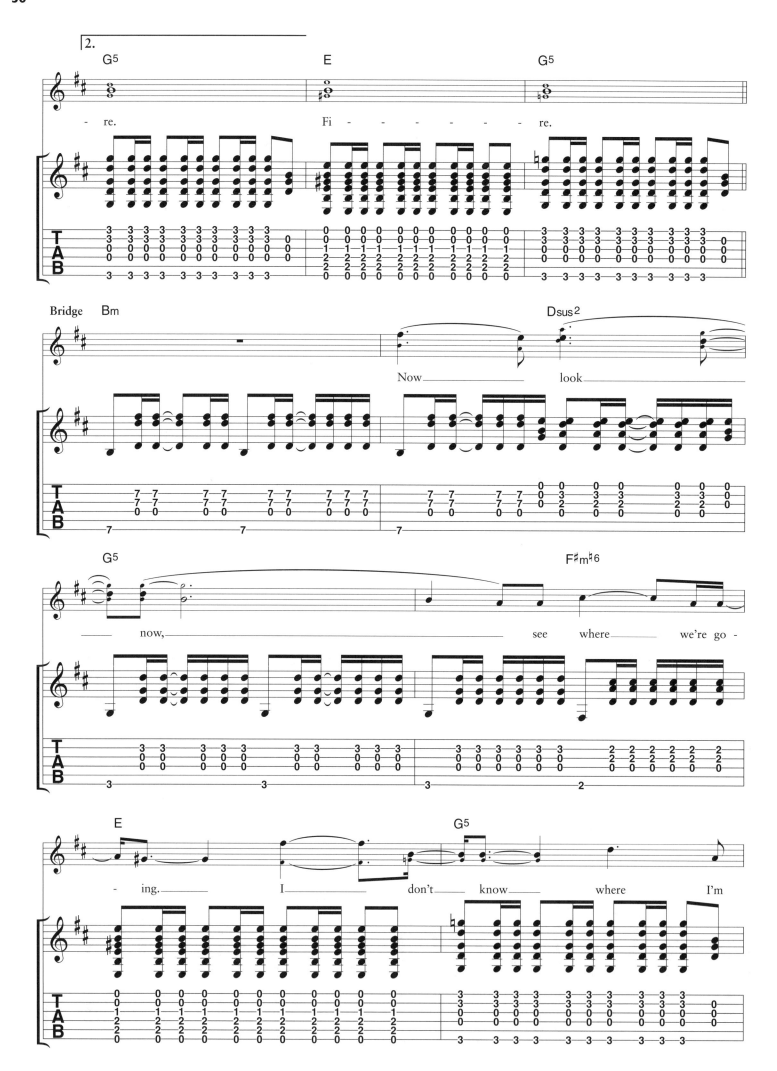

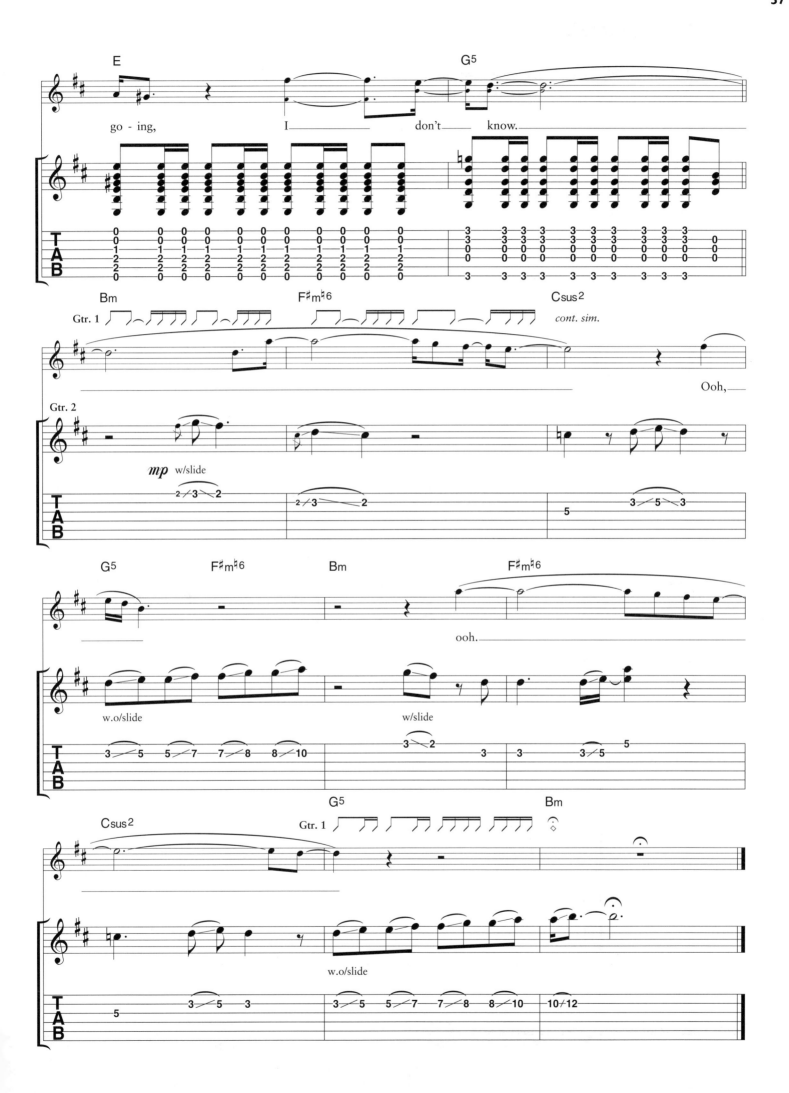

By TV Light

Words and Music by Olly Knights and Gale Paridjanian

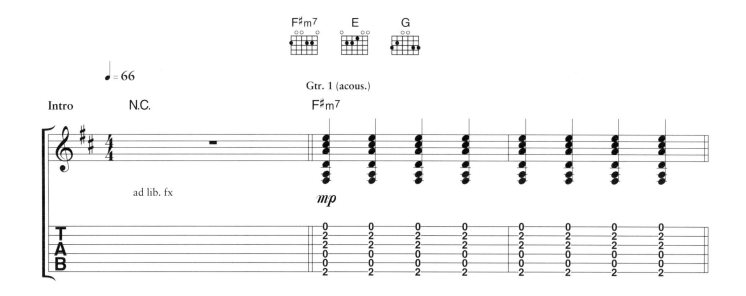

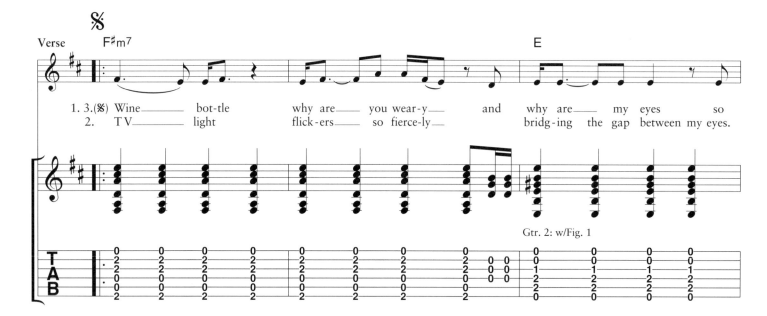

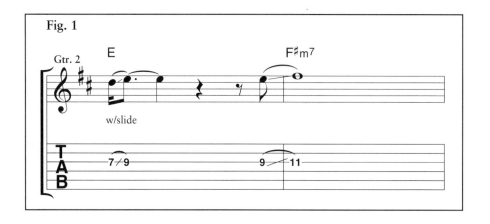

Fig. 1

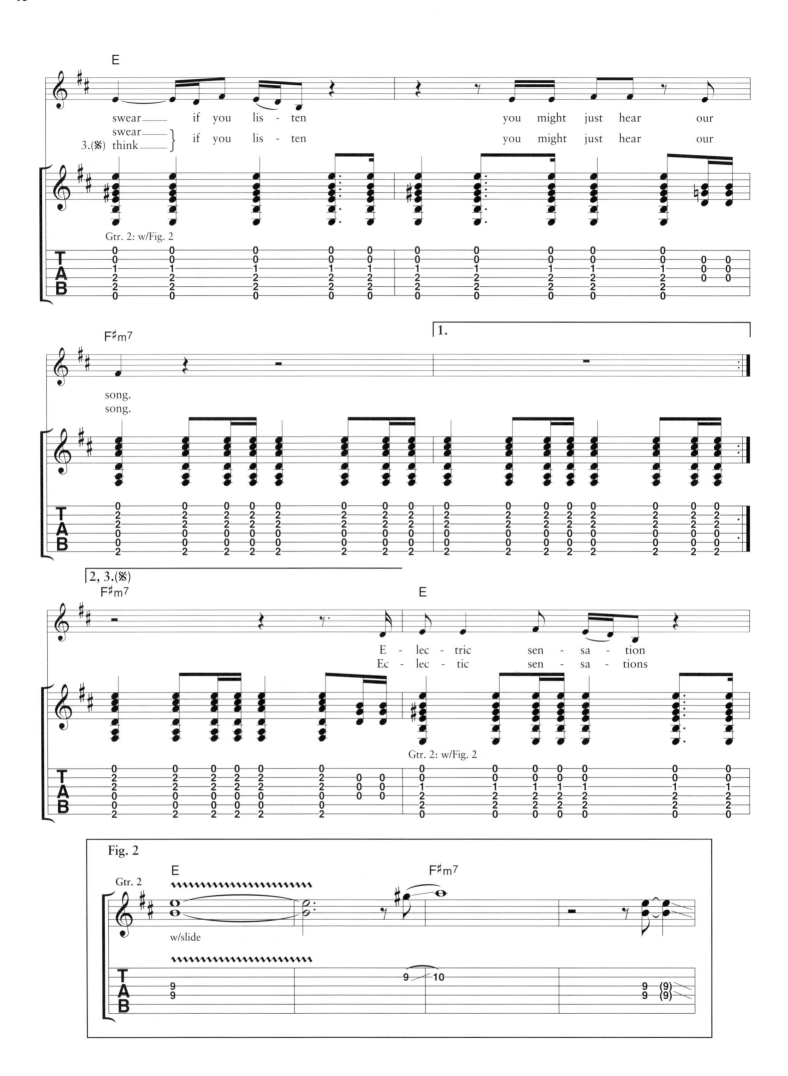

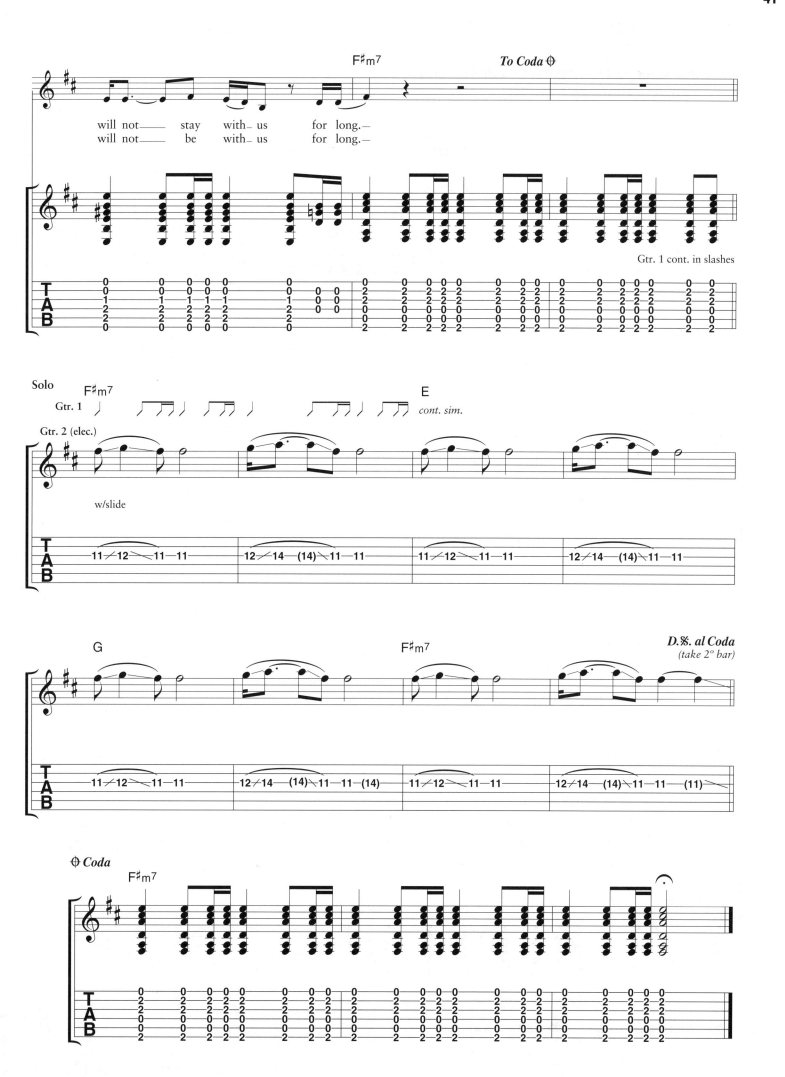

Starship

Words and Music by Olly Knights and Gale Paridjanian

Slack

Words and Music by Olly Knights and Gale Paridjanian

Verse

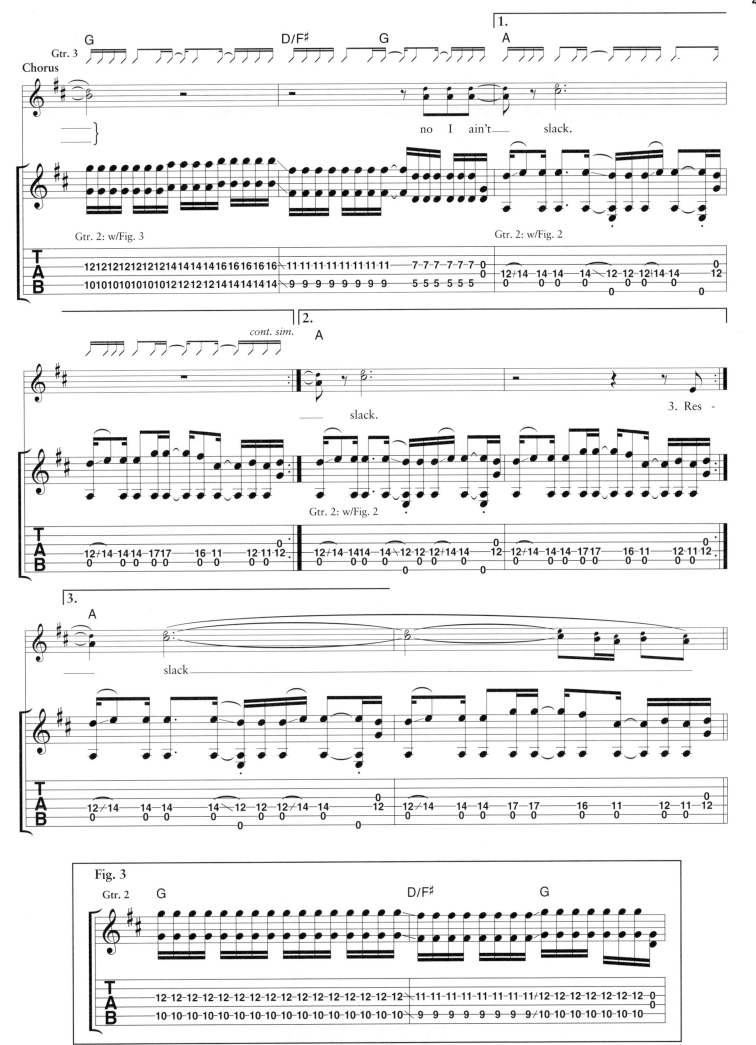

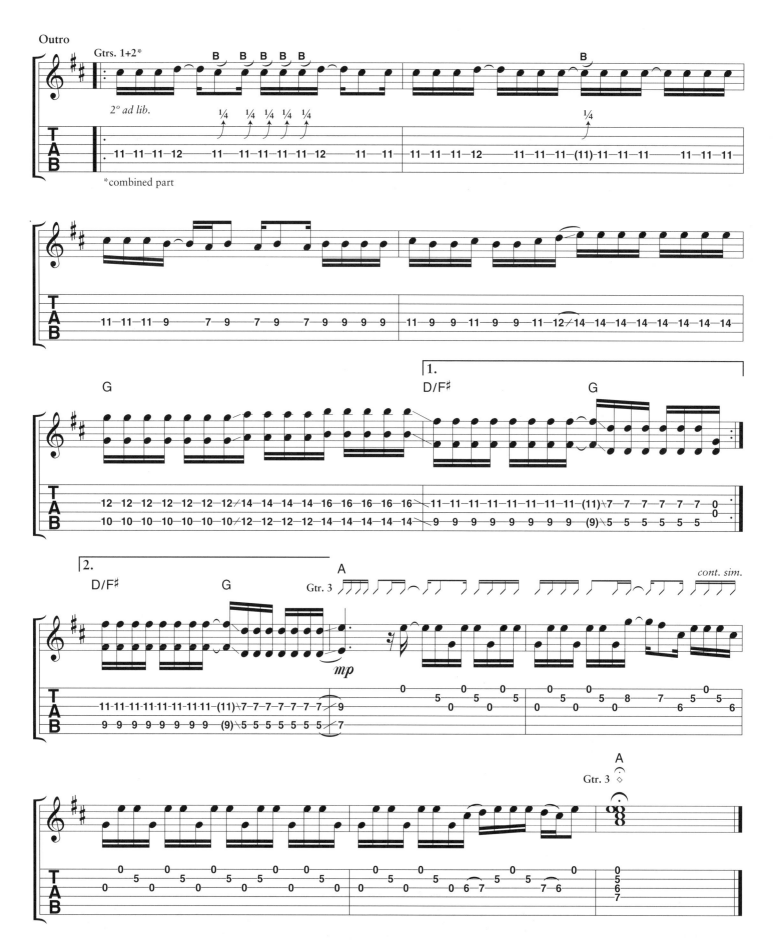

Verse 3:
Rescued a cat from a tree,
Its fur was all caked in dirt
But I killed it dead for liking me,
Yeah I stole a car and drove to town
And I know I ain't slack.

The Road

Words and Music by Olly Knights and Gale Paridjanian

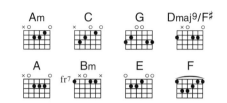

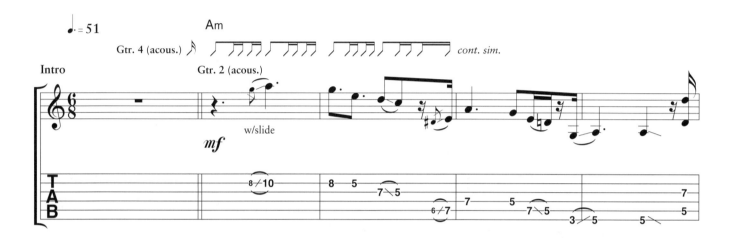

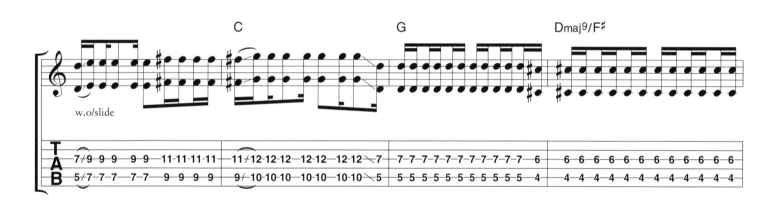

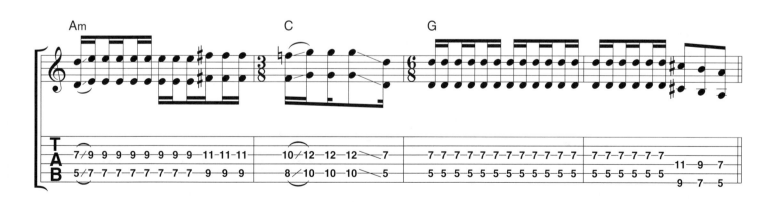

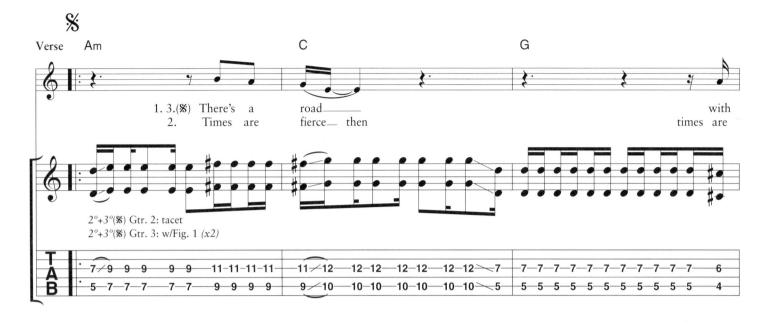

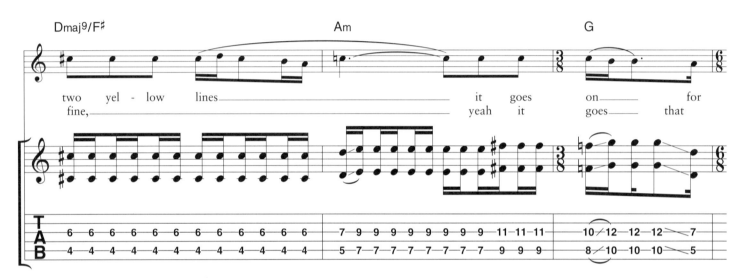

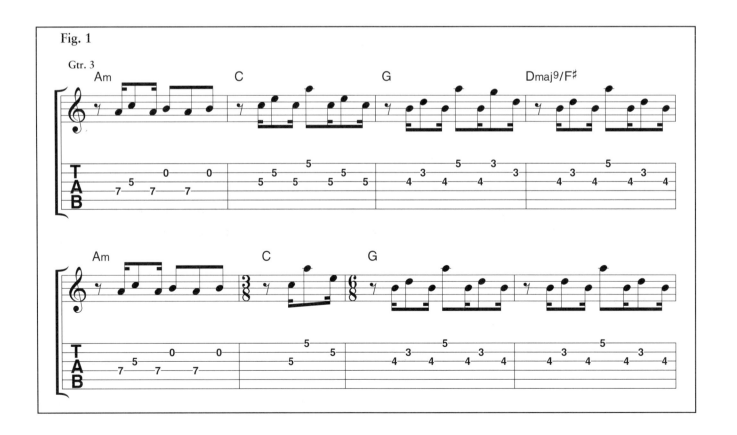

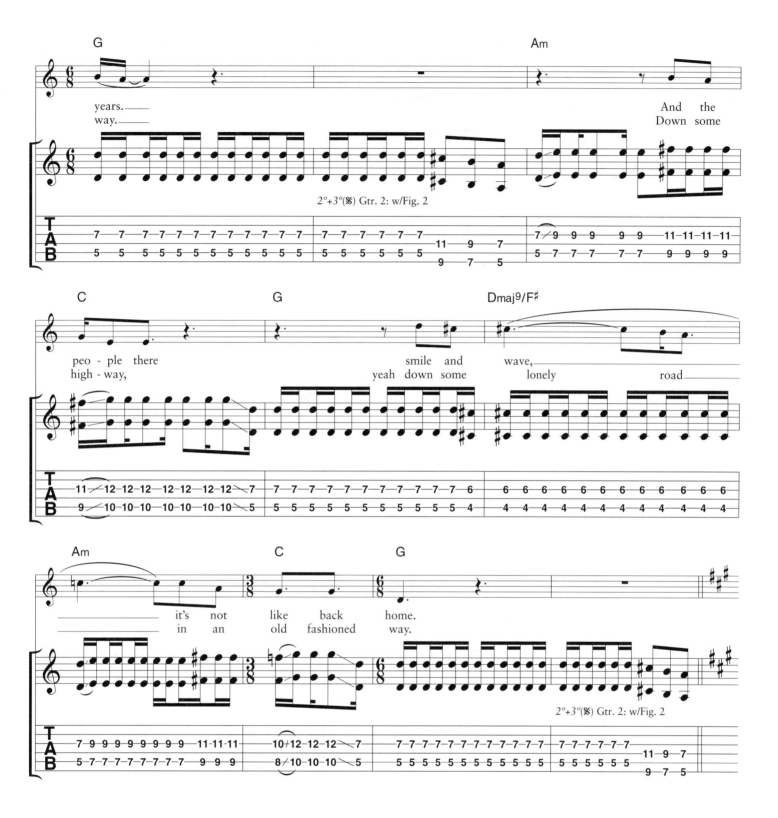

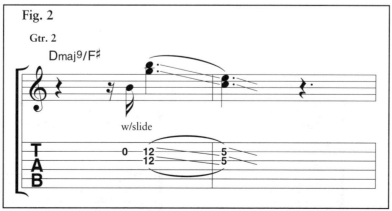

Mind Over Money

Words and Music by Olly Knights and Gale Paridjanian

Lyrics:

1. Mind ov-er mo-ney, bent ov-er back-wards light up my life like a ve-ry last style,

2. Wear-ing a smile like it's go-ing out of look at your-self ah, there's noth-ing in there

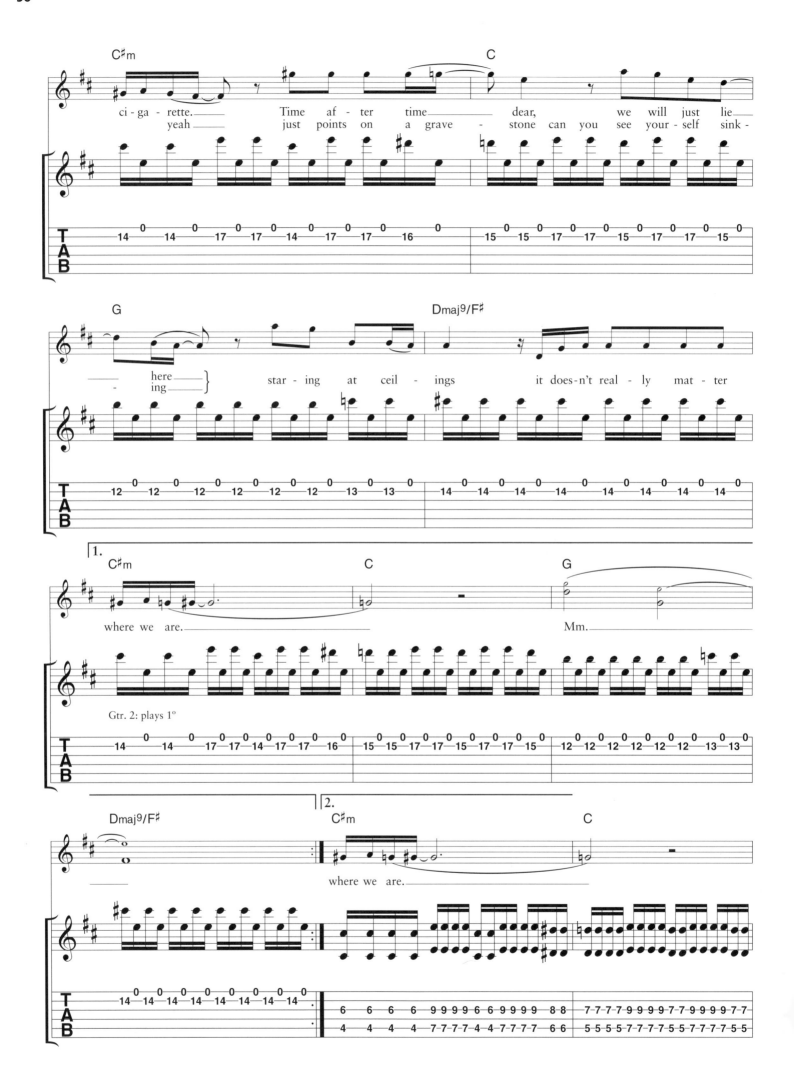

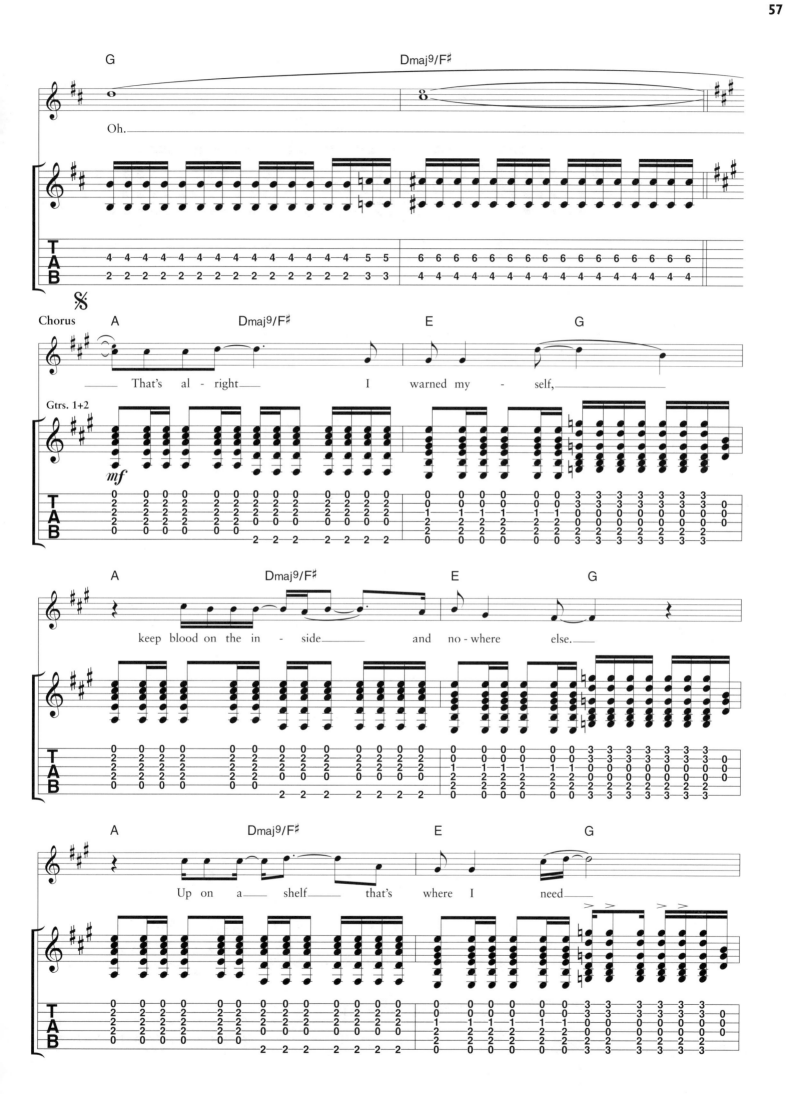

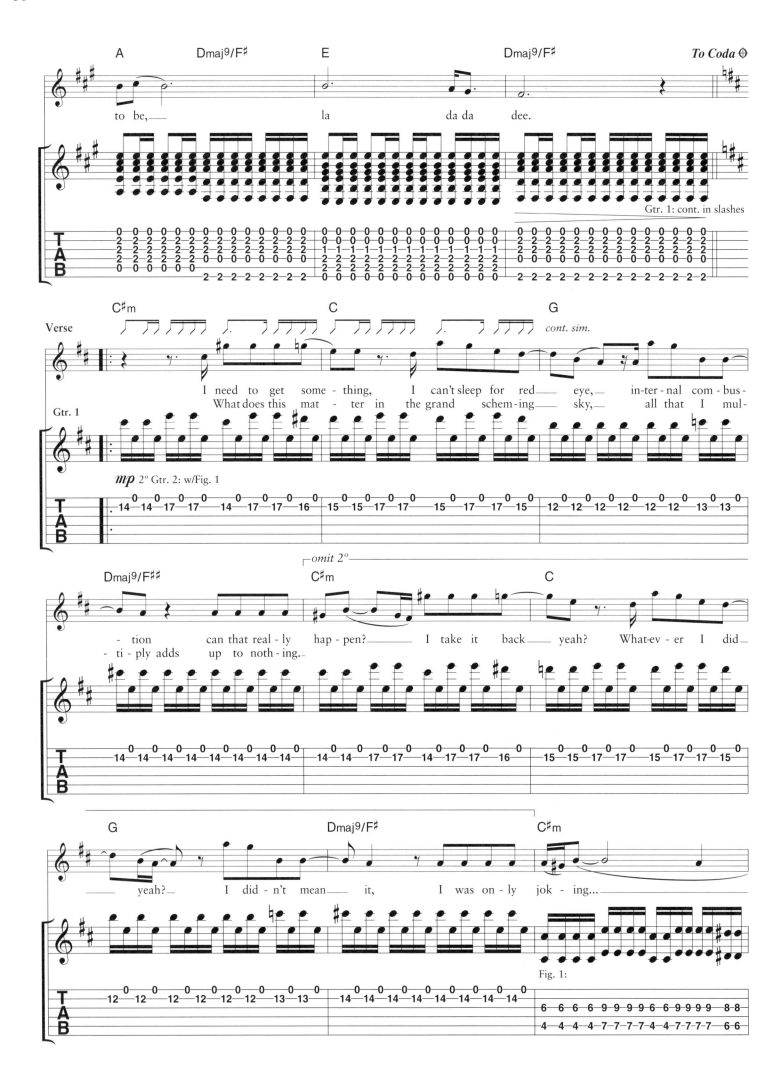

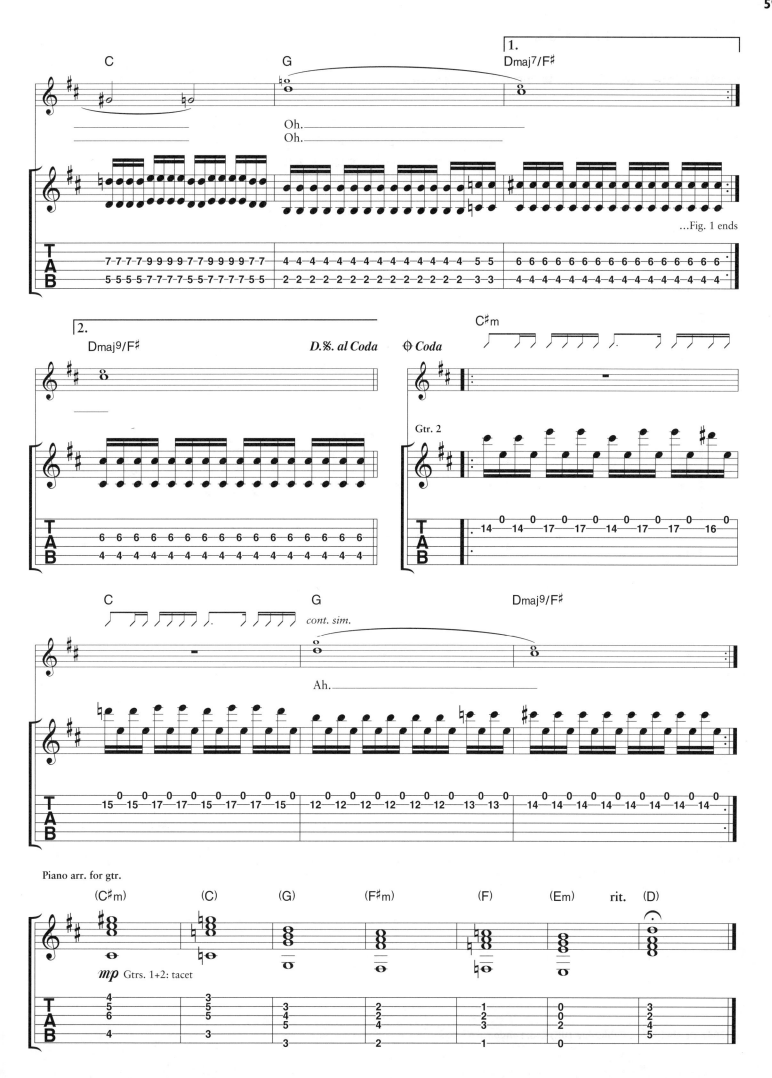

The Optimist

Words and Music by Olly Knights and Gale Paridjanian

Pre-chorus

Cracked skull with a creep-y mind____ in - side._____

I'm plan-ning the great - est of es - capes_____ you know.

Pa - tient - ly wait - ing in____ the line._____

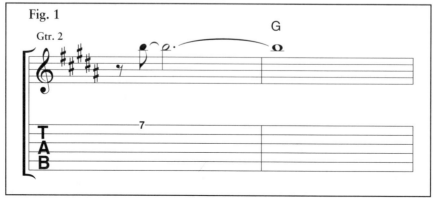

Fig. 1

Gtr. 2

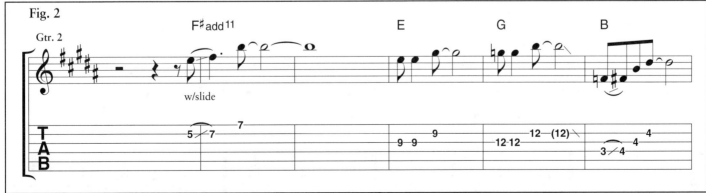

Three Days Old

Music by Olly Knights and Gale Paridjanian

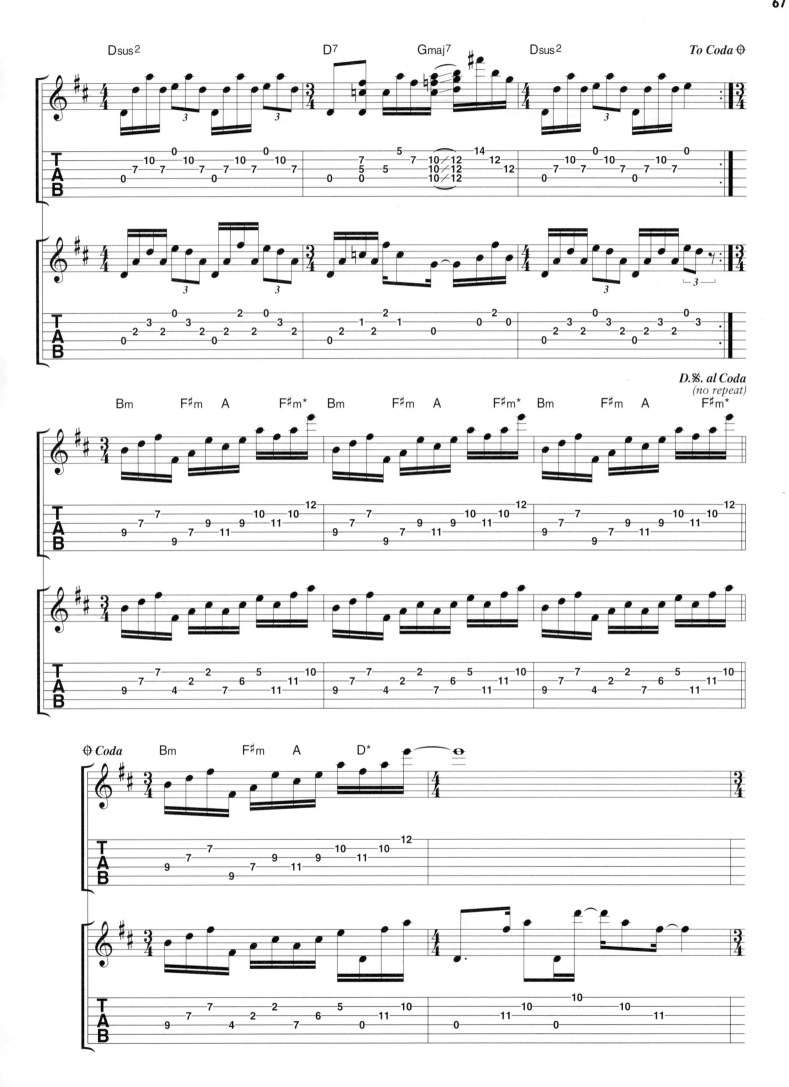